Magical Pets

A Practical Guide

AQUARIUM

FOR MY FAMILY

(AND PETS TOO)

MAGICAL PETS: A PRACTICAL GUIDE is a DAVID FICKLING BOOK
First published in Great Britain in 2018 by David Fickling Books, 31 Beaumont Street, Oxford, OX1 2NP
HB: 978 1 788450 30 0   PB: 978 1 788450 31 7
www.davidficklingbooks.com
Text and illustrations © Anya Glazer, 2018
1 3 5 7 9 10 8 6 4 2
The right of Anya Glazer to be identified as the author and illustrator of this work has been asserted
in accordance with the Copyright, Designs and Patents Act 1988.
All rights reserved.

WARNING: This book will make you pet crazy!

Papers used by David Fickling Books are from well-managed forests and other responsible sources.
DAVID FICKLING BOOKS Reg. No. 8340307
A CIP catalogue record for this book is available from the British Library.
Printed and bound in China by Toppan Leefung

Anya Glazer

Magical Pets

A Practical Guide

ENCHANTED EMPORIUM

db FICKLING
David Fickling Books

INVISIBLE BATS

PHOENIXES

FLYING MONKEYS

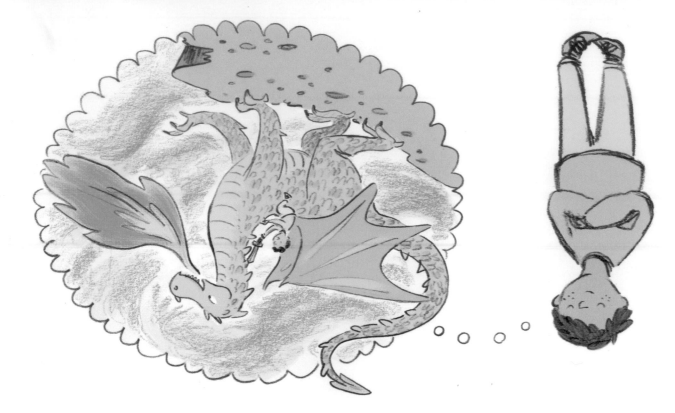

First things first . . .

be sure to choose your pet wisely.

(And remember they are choosing you too.)

Some pets will be harder work

than others . . .

. . . and some will be harder work
than most!

So, you will have to teach them some discipline.

You might even be able to

teach them a few tricks.

They'll need lots of exercise . . .

KEEP OFF
THE GRASS

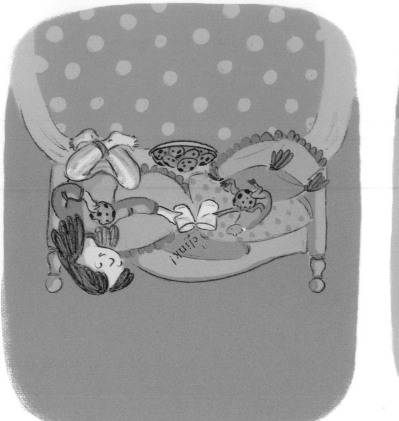

. . . and plenty to eat.

DOWN!

yuck!

Sometimes looking after your magical pet

gasp

poof

can be pretty tough . . .

pssht

They will be

your

VERY

best

friend . . .

. . . and they will never stop surprising you.